the view
hats off to the buskers

GW00658029

WISE PUBLICATIONS
part of The Music Sales Group
London / New York / Paris / Sydney / Copenhagen / Berlin / Madrid / Tokyo

Published by
Wise Publications
14-15 Berners Street, London, W1T 3LJ, UK.

Exclusive distributors:
Music Sales Limited
Distribution Centre, Newmarket Road,
Bury St Edmunds, Suffolk, IP33 3YB, UK.

Music Sales Pty Limited
120 Rothschild Avenue, Rosebery,
NSW 2018, Australia.

Order No. AM990242
ISBN 13: 978-1-84772-046-7
This book © Copyright 2007 Wise Publications,
a division of Music Sales Limited.

Edited by Tom Farncombe.
Music arranged by Martin Shellard.
Music processed by Paul Ewers Music Design.

Printed in the EU.

Your Guarantee of Quality:
As publishers, we strive to produce every book
to the highest commercial standards.

The running order of the songs matches the recorded album
and the music has been freshly engraved.

Particular care has been given to specifying
acid-free, neutral-sized paper made from pulps
which have not been elemental chlorine bleached.
This pulp is from farmed sustainable forests
and was produced with special regard for the environment.

Throughout, the printing and binding have
been planned to ensure a sturdy, attractive
publication which should give years of enjoyment.

If your copy fails to meet our high standards,
please inform us and we will gladly replace it.

www.musicsales.com

comin' down

Words & Music by
Kyle Falconer & Keiren Webster

1. I'm com -in'___ com -in' down.___
(2.) hear it,___ d'ya hear that sound?___

Took so long for me___ to come a - round.___
I hear that now a - loud,___ com -in' down.___

They tell you,__ it smash -es brain,__
I'm not ea - ger___ to be mean.__

drain you of all the blood___
Ea - ger to be an -

makes me think   we'll nev-er   last.____   Na,   na - na-na, na, na,   na.

Chorus

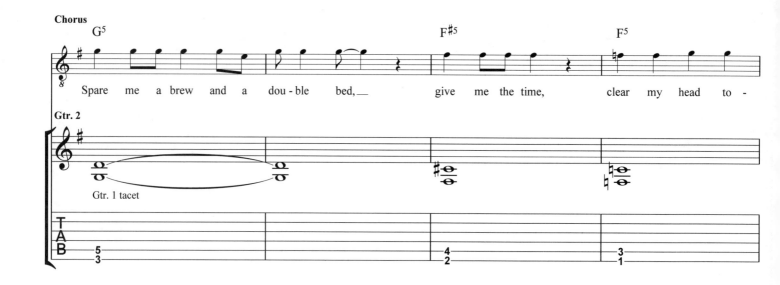

Spare me a brew and a dou-ble bed, ___ give me the time, clear my head to -

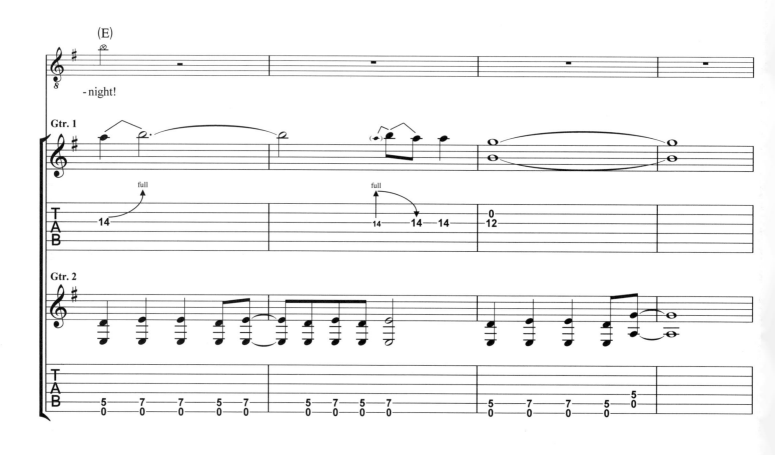

-night!

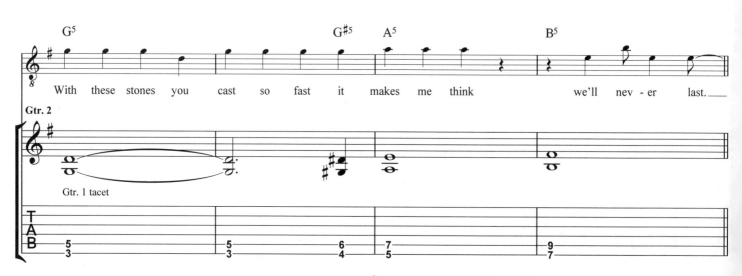

With these stones you cast so fast it makes me think we'll nev-er last. ___

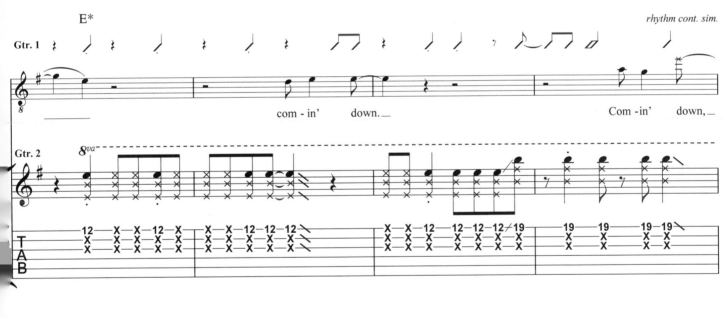

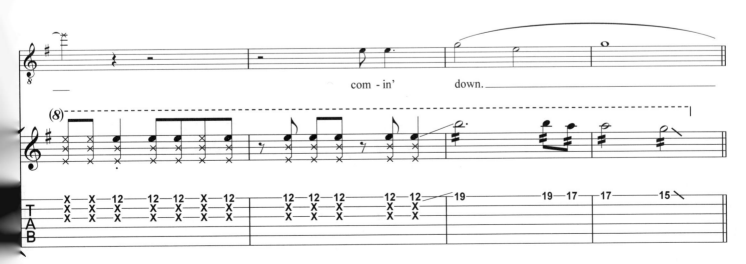

10

Outro

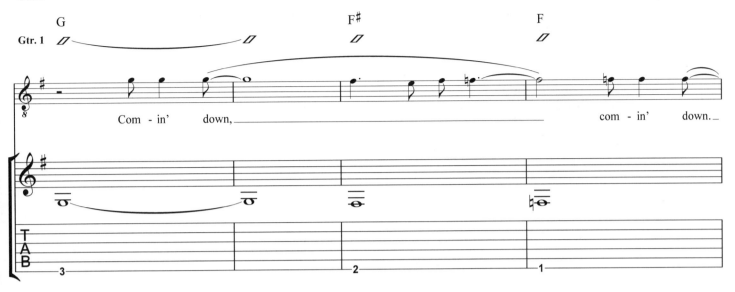

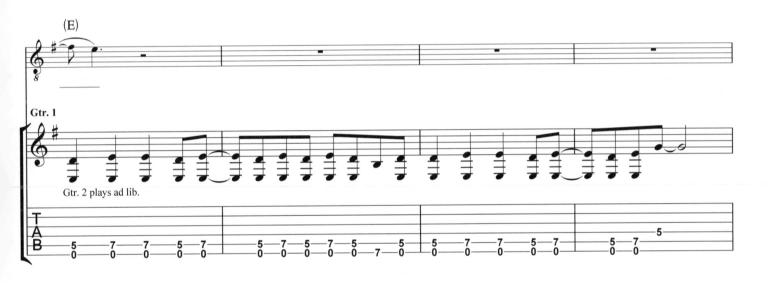

11

superstar tradesman

Words & Music by
Kyle Falconer & Keiren Webster

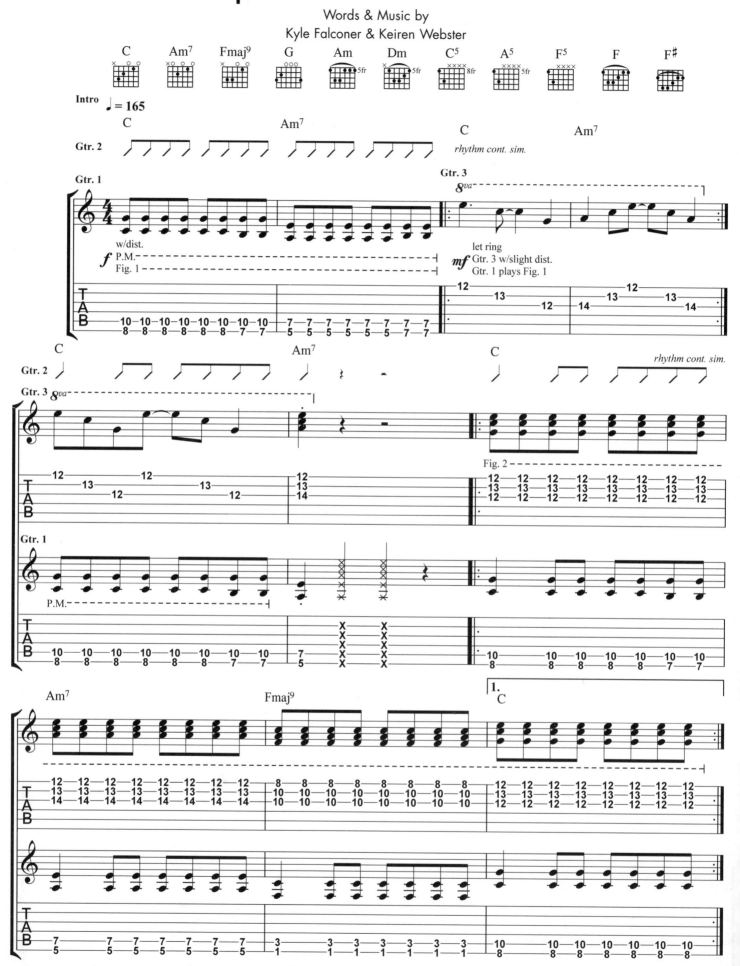

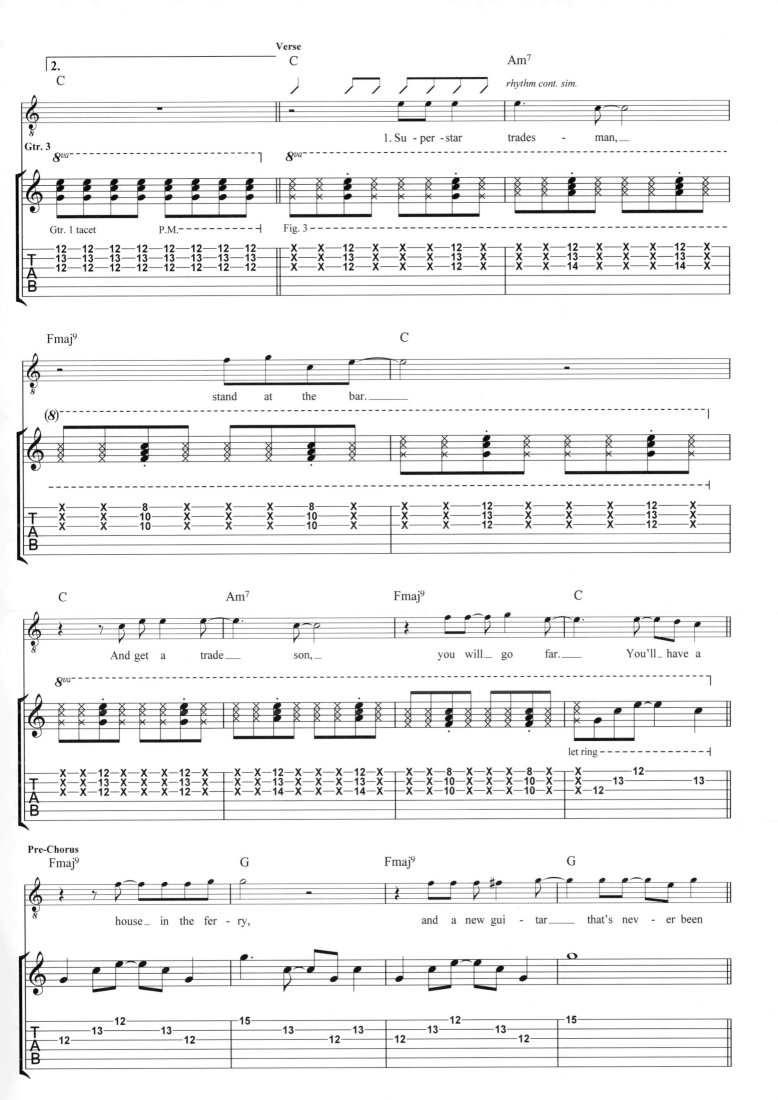

14

17

same jeans

Words & Music by
Kyle Falconer & Keiren Webster

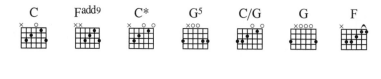

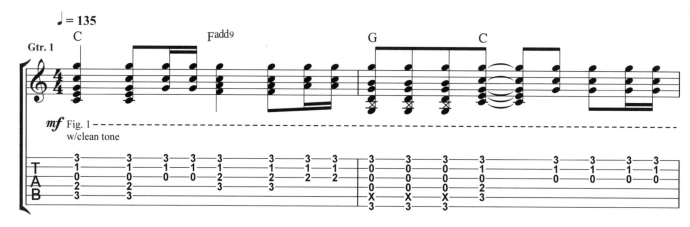

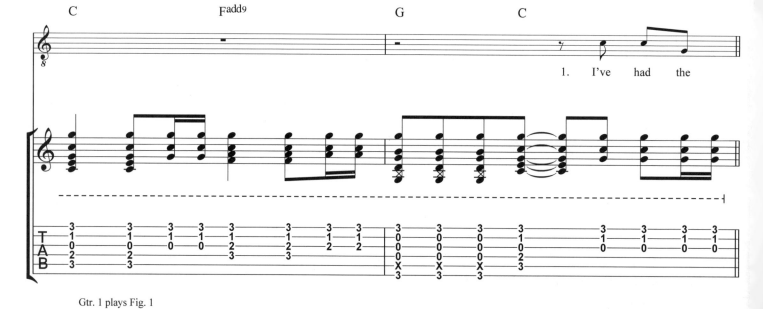

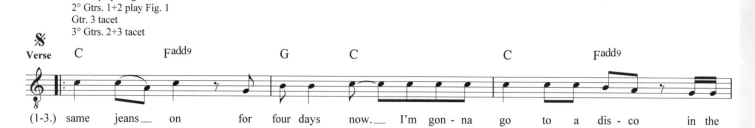

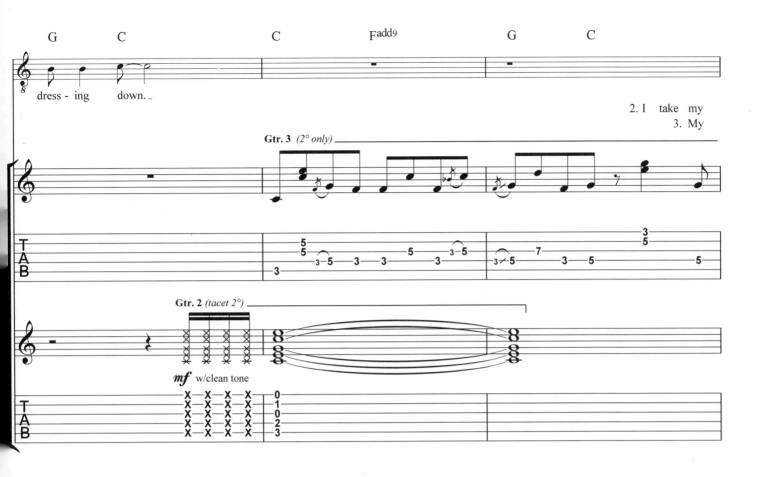

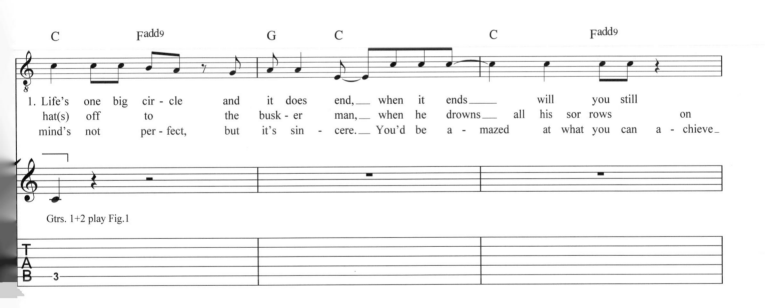

I'm not mak - ing a fool of my - self.___ So,
___ me, he's smil - ing as long as he can.___
___ you try so hard but your heart's___ on a switch.___

Gtr. 3 *(tacet 1°)*

Gtr. 3 *(1° only)*

mf w/slight dist.

Chorus

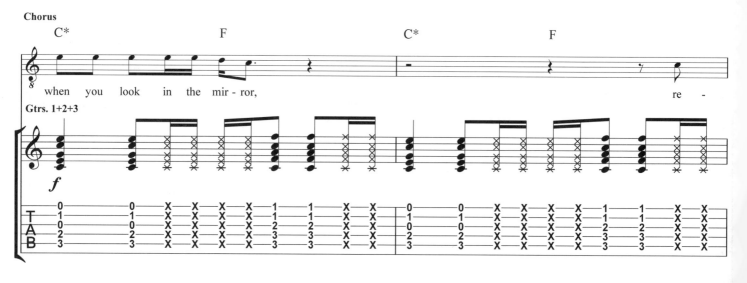

when you look in the mir - ror, re -

Gtrs. 1+2+3

f

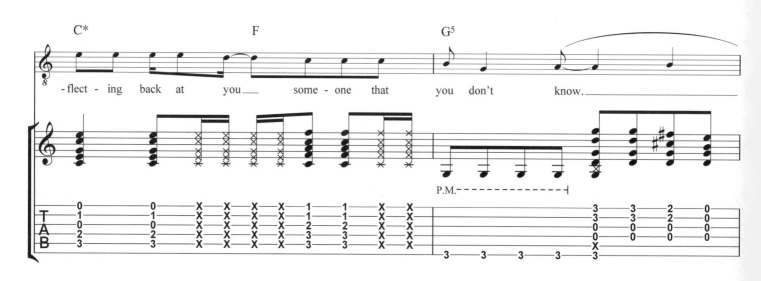

-flect - ing back at you___ some - one that you don't know.___

P.M.

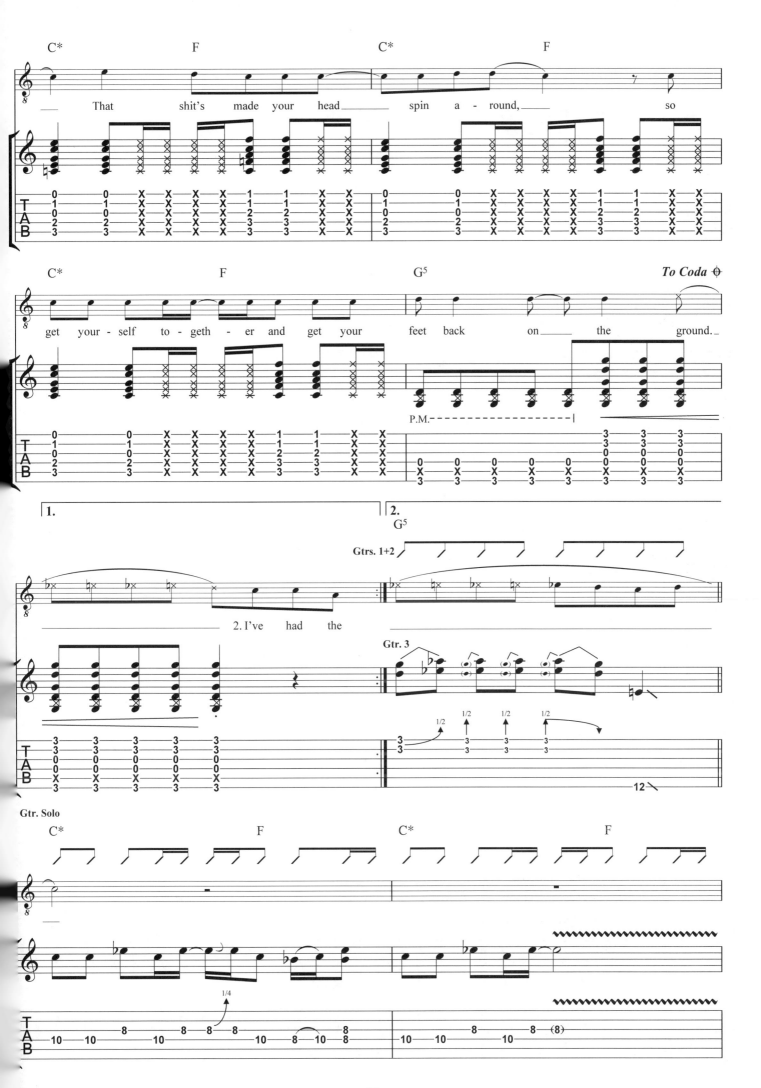

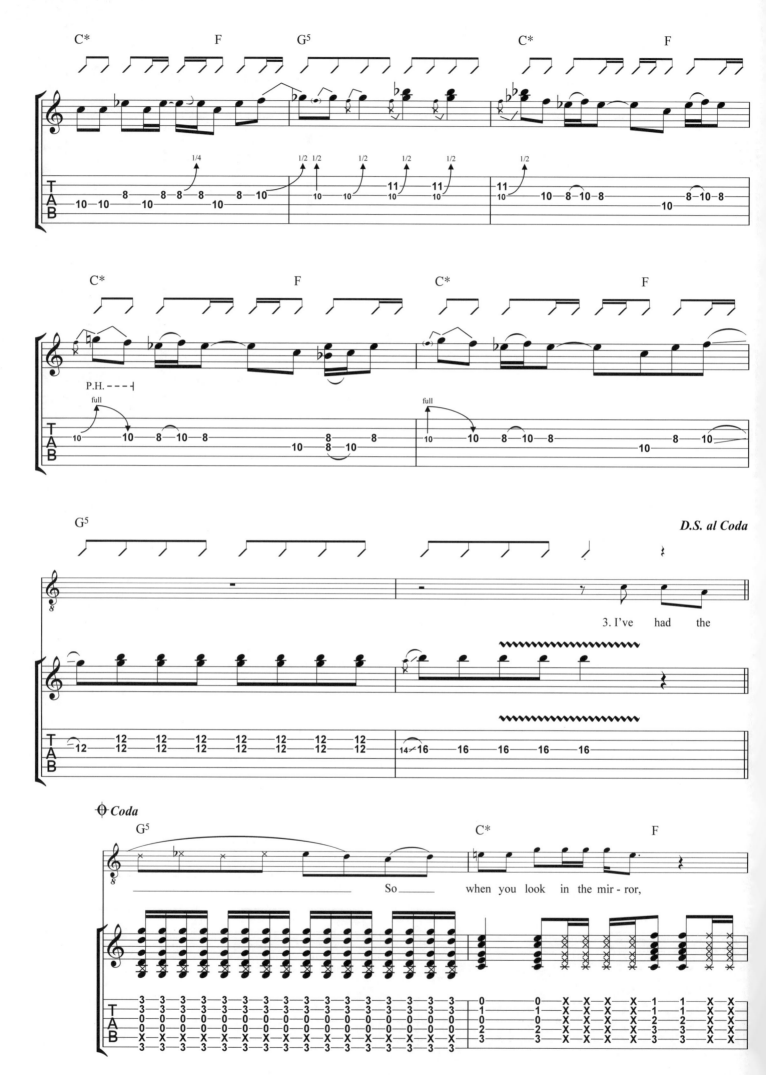

3. I've had the

Coda

So_____ when you look in the mir - ror,

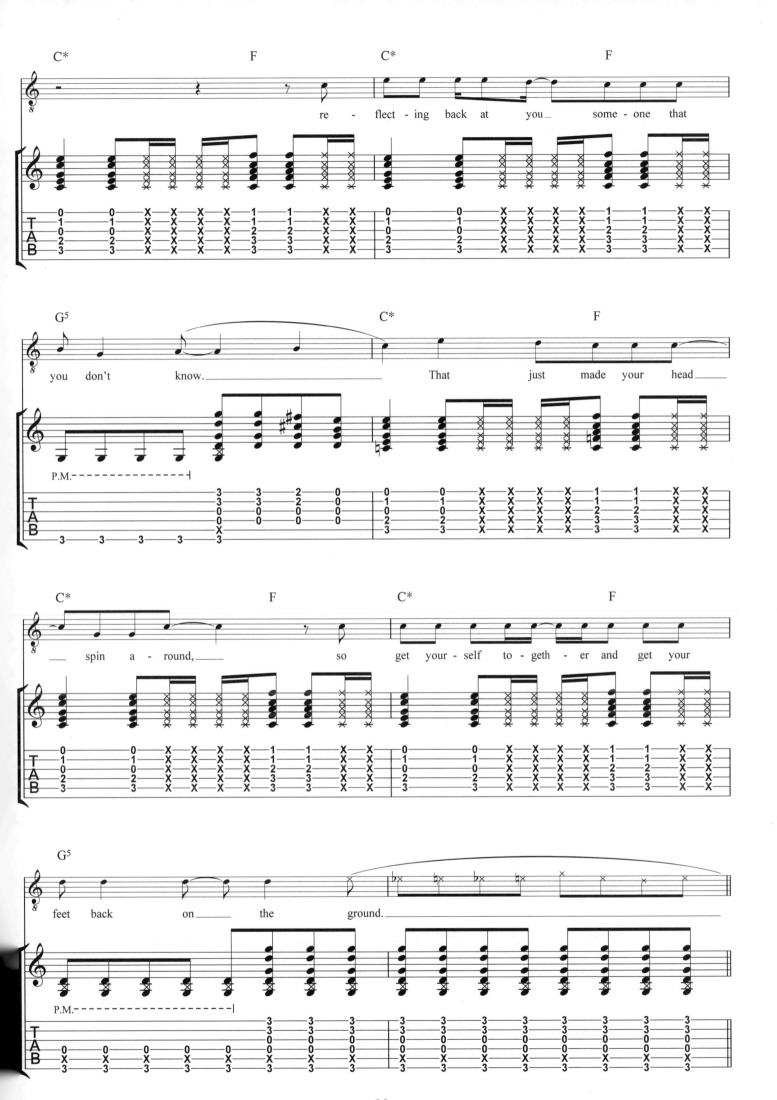

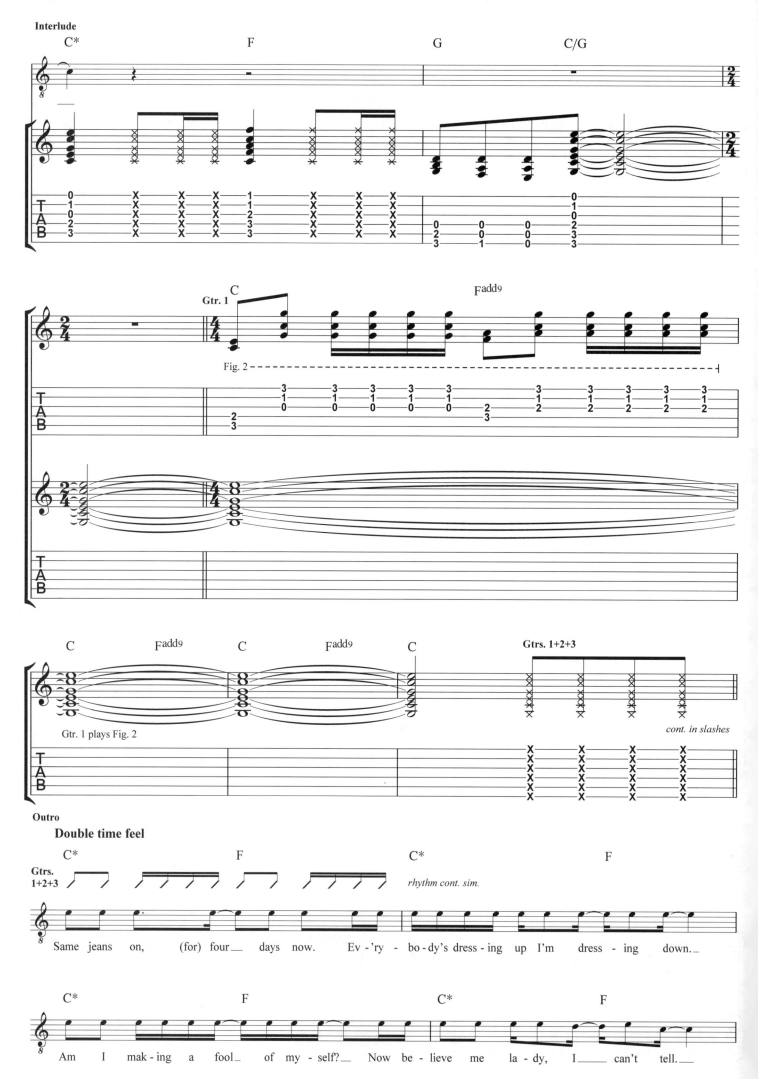

Outro
Double time feel

Same jeans on, (for) four days now. Ev-'ry-bo-dy's dress-ing up I'm dress-ing down.

Am I mak-ing a fool of my-self? Now be-lieve me la-dy, I can't tell.

24

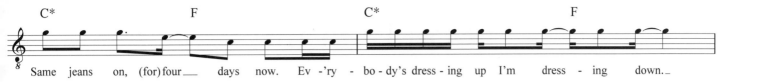

Same jeans on, (for) four days now. Ev -'ry - bo - dy's dress - ing up I'm dress - ing down._

Am I mak - ing a fool_ of my - self?_ be - lieve me la - dy, I_ can't tell._

Gtr. 3

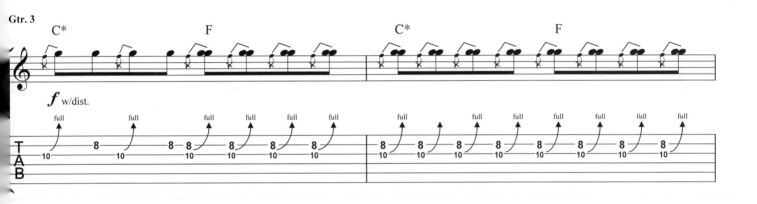

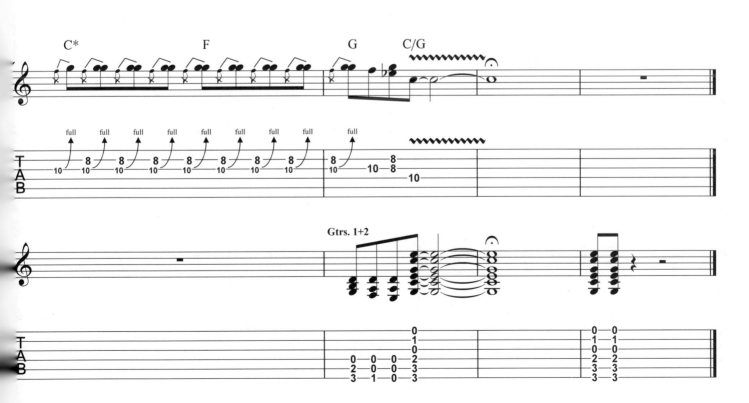

don't tell me

Words & Music by
Kyle Falconer & Keiren Webster

Interlude

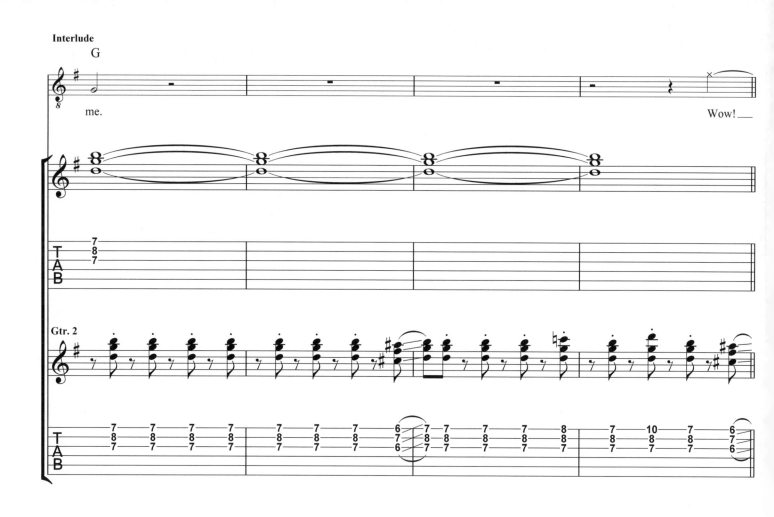

Gtr. solo

30

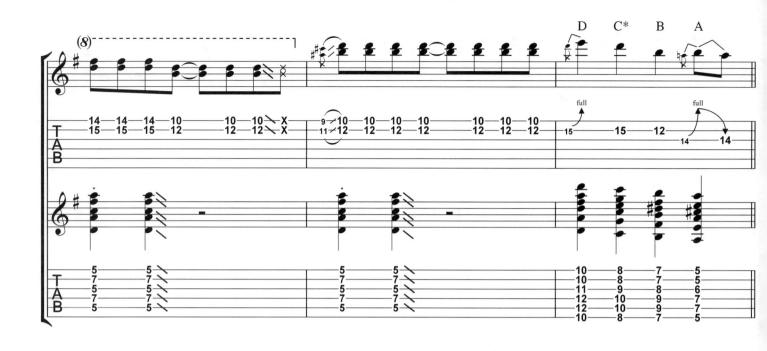

D.S. al Coda

Interlude

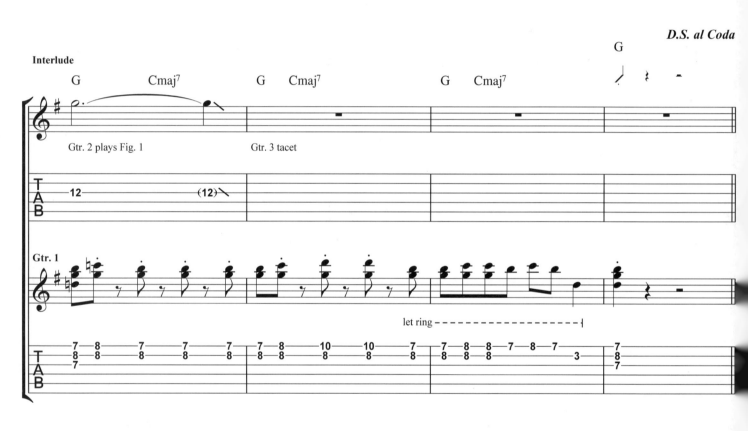

Gtr. 2 plays Fig. 1

Gtr. 3 tacet

Gtr. 1

let ring ---------------------⌐

⊕ Coda

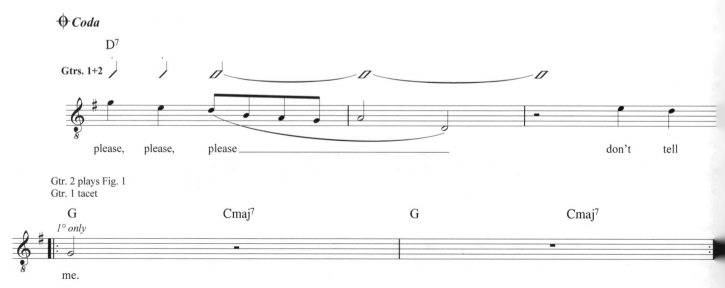

Gtrs. 1+2

please,   please,   please _____   don't   tell

Gtr. 2 plays Fig. 1
Gtr. 1 tacet

G   Cmaj⁷   G   Cmaj⁷

1° only

me.

skag trendy

Words & Music by
Kyle Falconer & Keiren Webster

37

the don

Words & Music by
Kyle Falconer & Keiren Webster

Oh, what a soft touch of a boy. ___ He'd wan - der with pride to   sell, _ and keep
In - vest - ed life in me - di - cine, ___ which is-n't the wis-est way to go.   Had so   much shit go - ing on,   con -
Oh, what a soft touch of a don. ___ He'd wan - der with pride to   sell, _ and keep

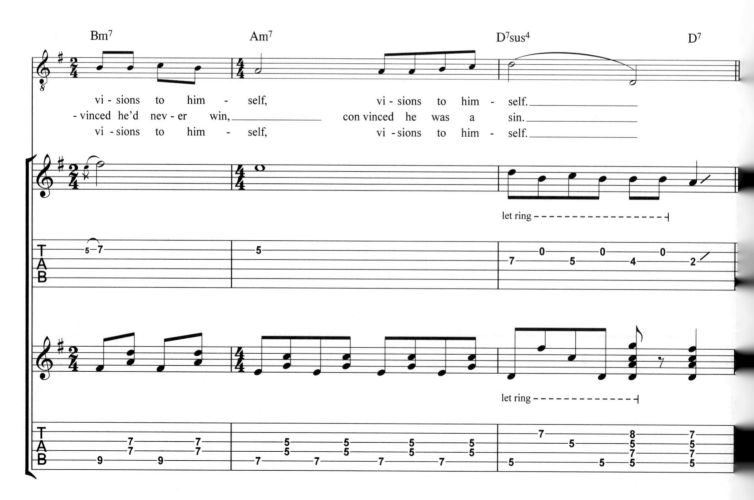

vi - sions to him - self,   vi - sions to him - self. _____
- vinced he'd nev - er win, _____   con vinced he was a   sin. _____
vi - sions to him - self,   vi - sions to him - self. _____

let ring -------------------

let ring -------------

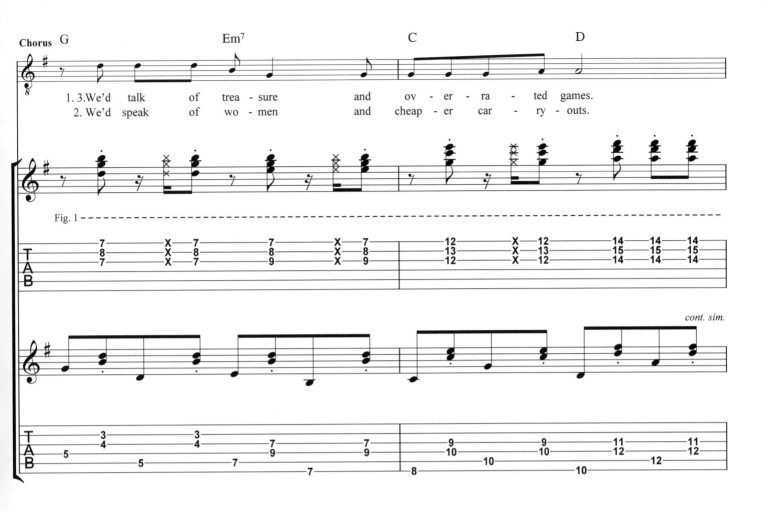

Chorus

1. 3.We'd talk of trea - sure and ov - er - ra - ted games.
2. We'd speak of wo - men and cheap - er car - ry - outs.

Fig. 1

cont. sim.

We'd steal the milk bot -tles, sneak -ing through the back 'round Jim - my's way.
We'd turn up to all the fes - ti - vals, tryin' to bring down the touts.

To Coda

let ring

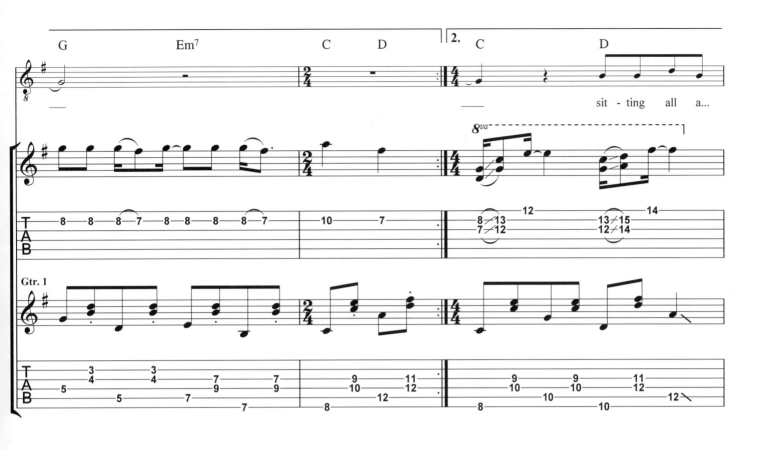

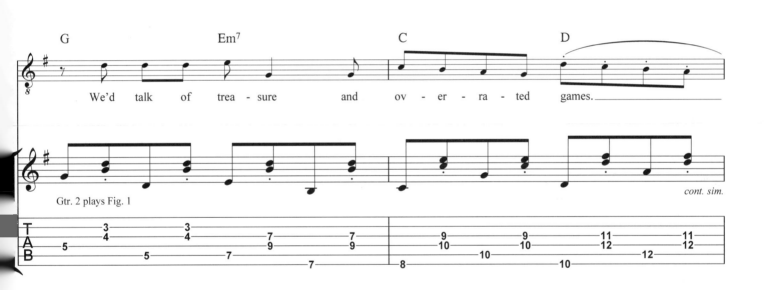

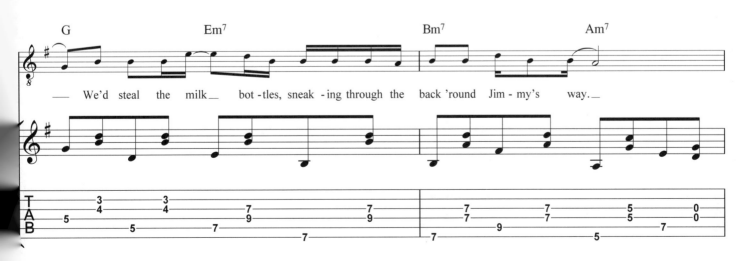

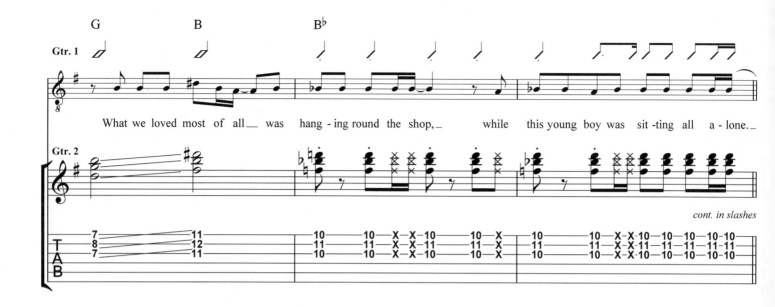

Bridge

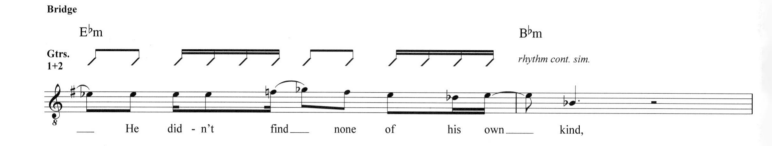

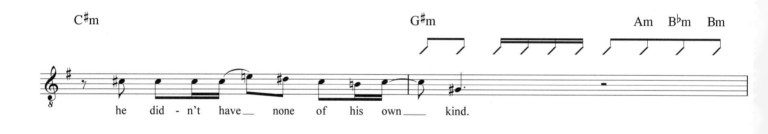

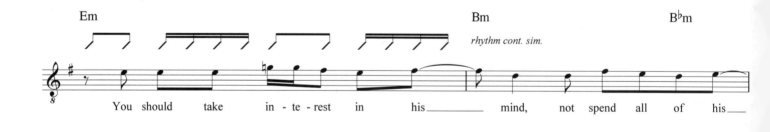

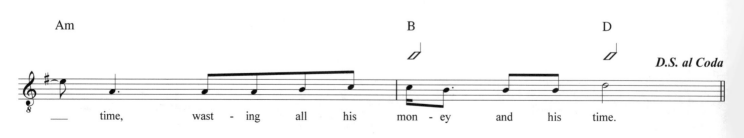

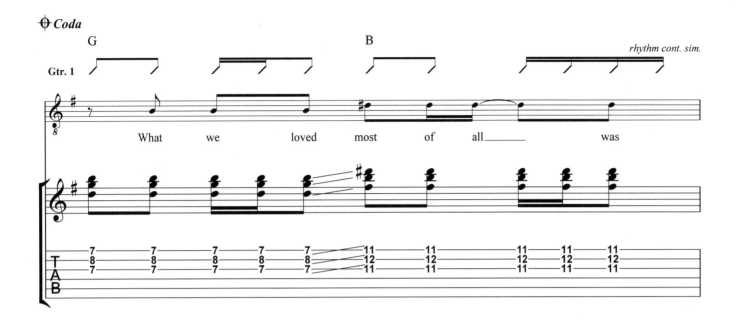

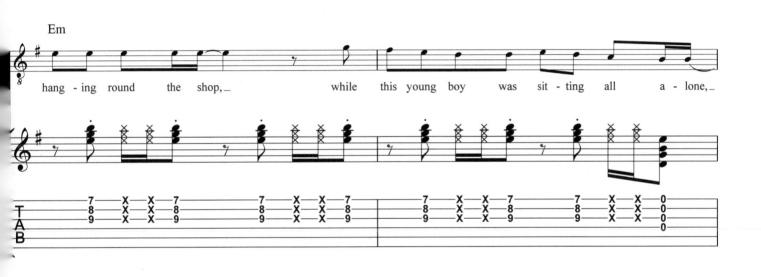

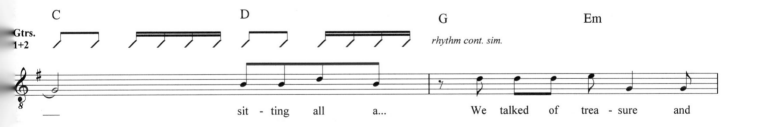

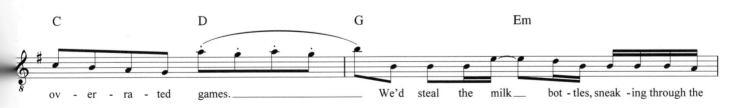

47

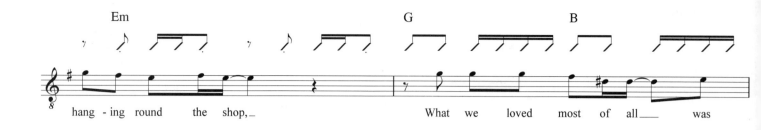

hang - ing round the shop, __ What we loved most of all __ was

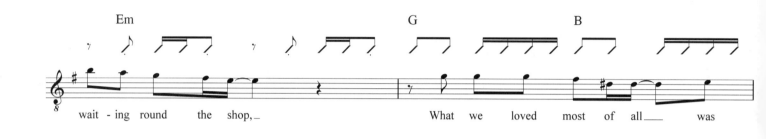

wait - ing round the shop, __ What we loved most of all __ was

rall.

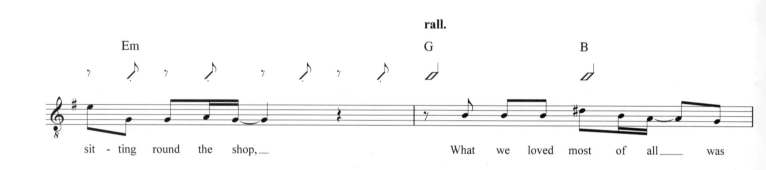

sit - ting round the shop, __ What we loved most of all __ was

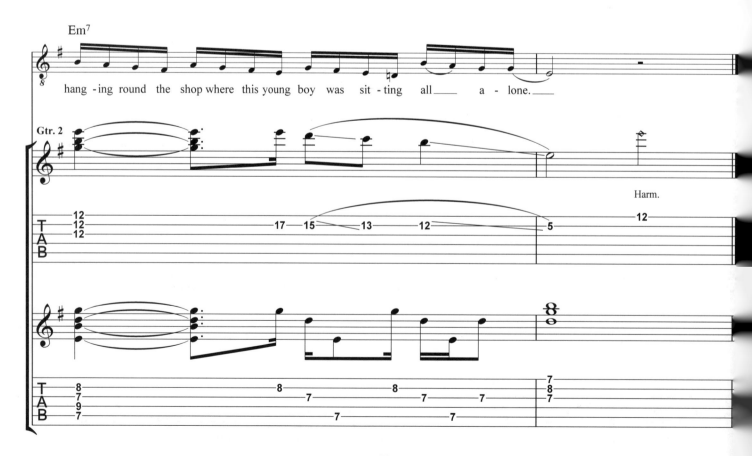

hang - ing round the shop where this young boy was sit - ting all __ a - lone. __

face for the radio

Words & Music by
Kyle Falconer & Keiren Webster

Verse

3. He watch - es 'Train - spot - ting' fif - teen times a week,__
4. P. C. on sum mer nights, foot - ball in the rain.__

Gtr. 2 (acous.)

mf let ring...
Fig. 1

Gtr. 2 plays Fig. 1

think - ing it's mak ing him__ whoa, so u - nique.__
Does - n't mat - ter how__ far he is,__ he's al - ways mon - ey for__ the train.

Which way will you go?__

Gtr. 2

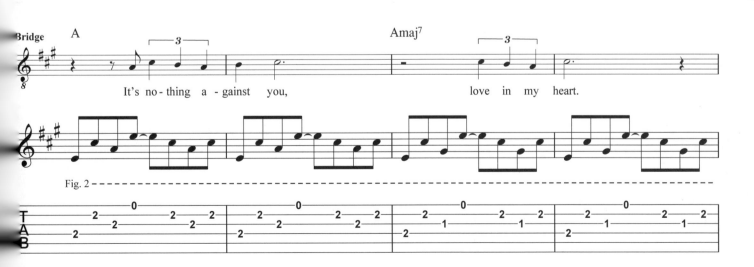

Bridge

It's no - thing a - gainst you, love in my heart.

Fig. 2

You're real - ly a nice___ guy,

known it from___ the start.____

Gtr. 2 plays Fig. 2

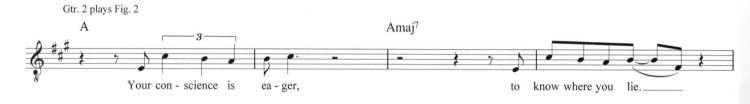

Your con - science is ea - ger,

to know where you lie.___

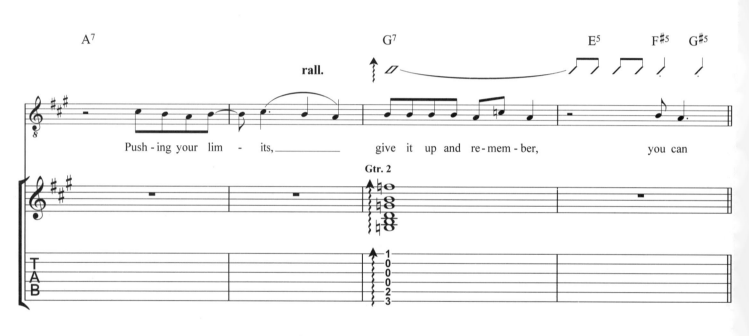

rall.

Push - ing your lim - its,_____ give it up and re - mem - ber, you can

Gtr. 2

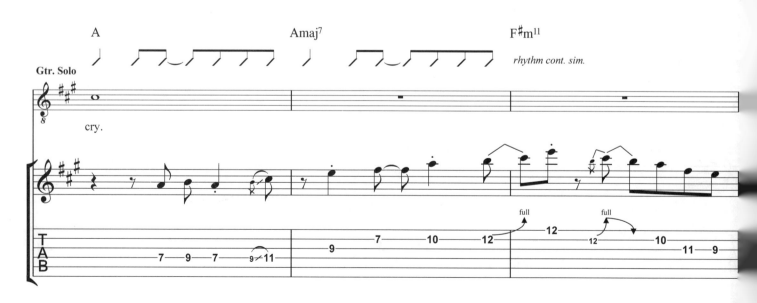

Gtr. Solo

rhythm cont. sim.

cry.

full   full

wasted little dj's

Words & Music by
Kyle Falconer & Keiren Webster

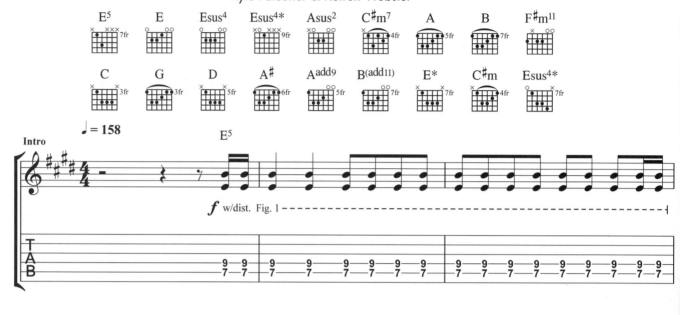

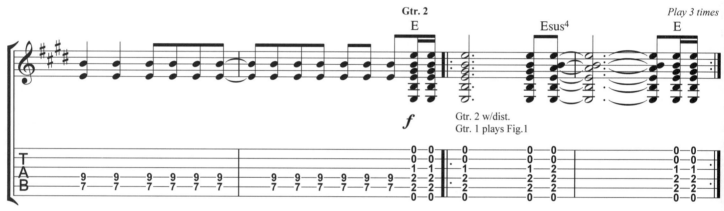

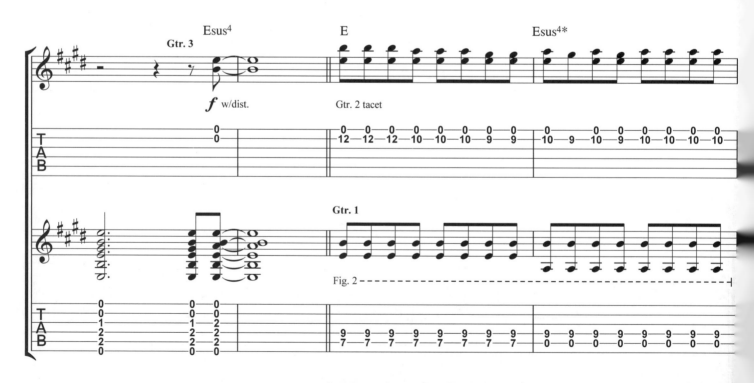

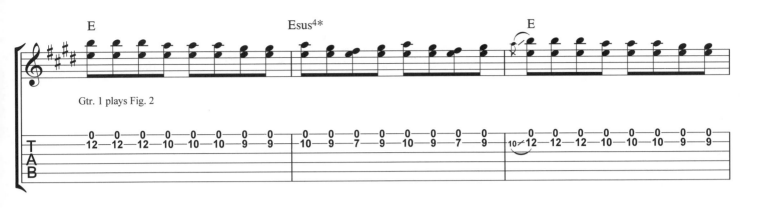

Gtr. 1 plays Fig. 2

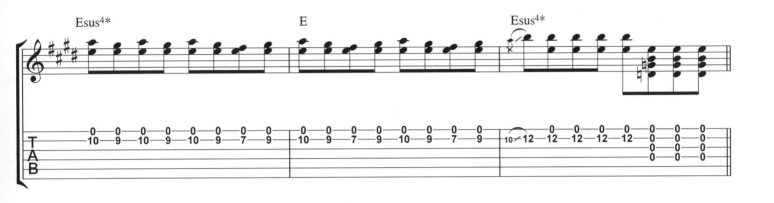

Gtr. 3 tacet
Gtr. 2 tacet *2°*

Verse

rhythm cont. sim.

1. They told me, if I write this song for them,___ that they would
2. Split vi-sions of a talk-a-tive the-ra - py,___ it makes you

cut my hair for free,___ but that's not me,___ no li - ber - ties.___
bend a - way, he gives me E.___ Seems hard to say,___ this in - sa - ni - ty.___

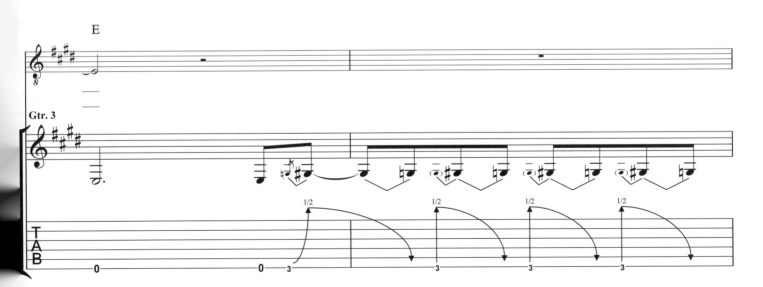

Gtr. 3

55

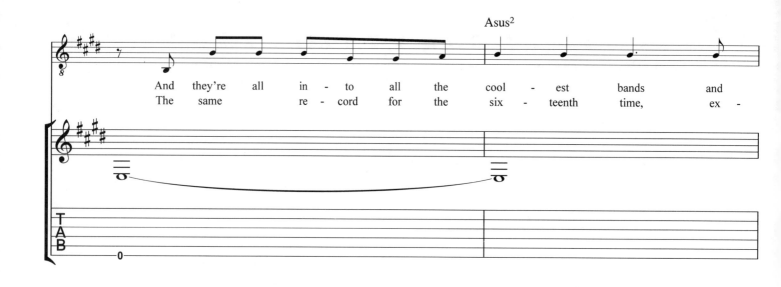

Asus²

And they're all in - to all the cool - est bands and
The same re - cord for the six - teenth time, ex -

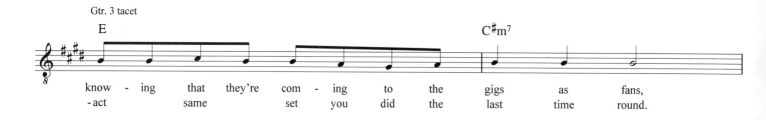

Gtr. 3 tacet

E   C♯m⁷

know - ing that they're com - ing to the gigs as fans,
-act same set you did the last time round.

A   B

en - ti - tles me_____ to some de - cen - cy.
does - n't bo - ther me,_____ we're in har - mo - ny._____

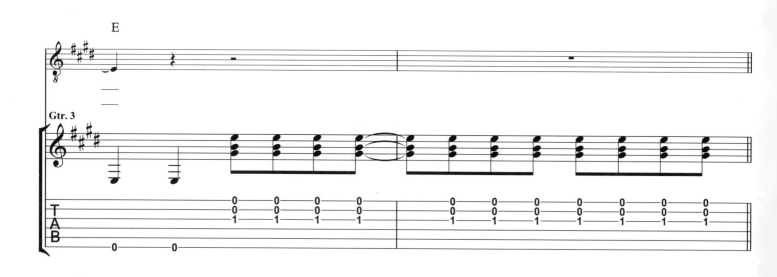

E

Gtr. 3

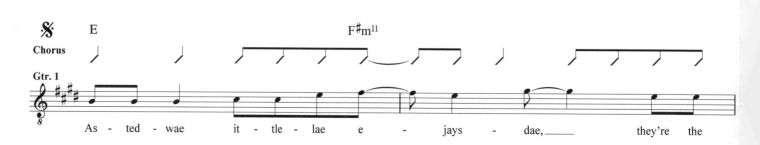

𝄋 E   F♯m¹¹

Chorus

Gtr. 1

As - ted - wae it - tle - lae e - jays - dae,_____ they're the

56

57

gran's for tea

Words & Music by
Kyle Falconer & Keiren Webster

62

64

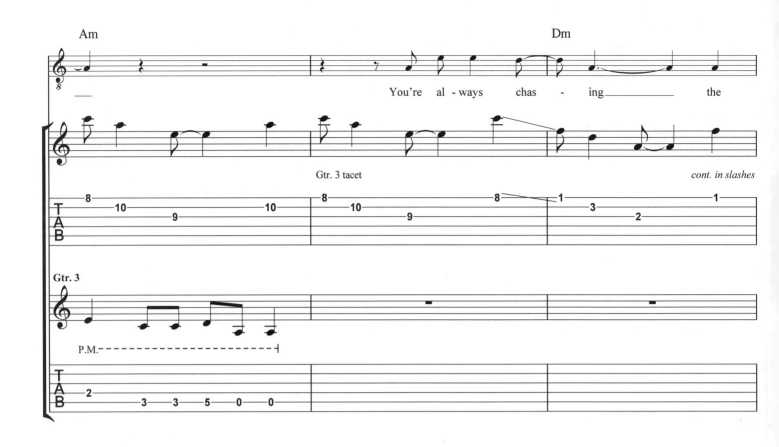

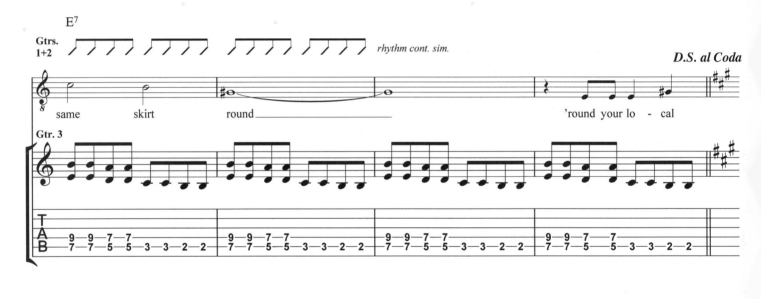

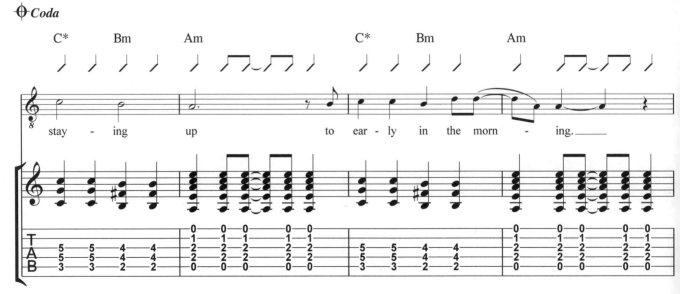

66

Oh, _____ ow, wow, wow, wow,

Outro

wow!

Gtr. 2

let ring...
Gtr. 1 plays Fig. 1
Gtr. 3 tacet

Mile long queue in the chip - py, I wish I ___ was at my Gran's for tea.

These peo - ple call me their friends but they don't ___ think the same as _____ me.

dance into the night

Words & Music by
Kyle Falconer & Keiren Webster

Gtr. 2 plays Fig. 2

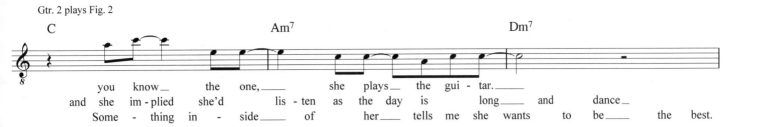

you know___ the one,___ she plays___ the gui - tar.___
and she im - plied she'd lis - ten as the day is long___ and dance___
Some - thing in - side___ of her___ tells me she wants to be___ the best.

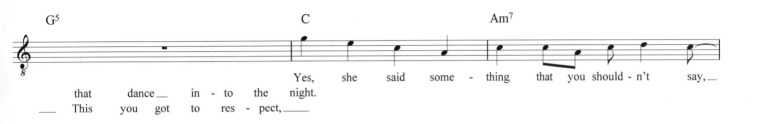

that dance___ in - to the night. Yes, she said some - thing that you should - n't say, ___
___ This you got to res - pect,___

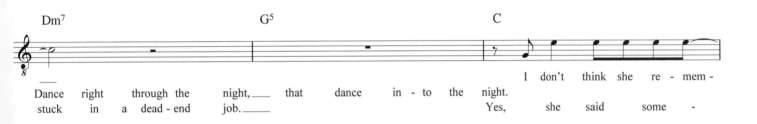

___ Dance right through the night,___ that dance in - to the night. I don't think she re - mem -
stuck in a dead - end job.___ Yes, she said some -

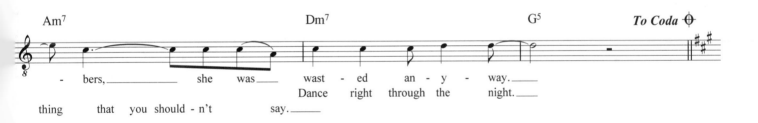

- bers,___ she was___ wast - ed an - y - way.___
Dance right through the night.___
thing that you should - n't say.___

Chorus

Gtr. 3 — *f* w/dist. — *rhythm cont. sim.*

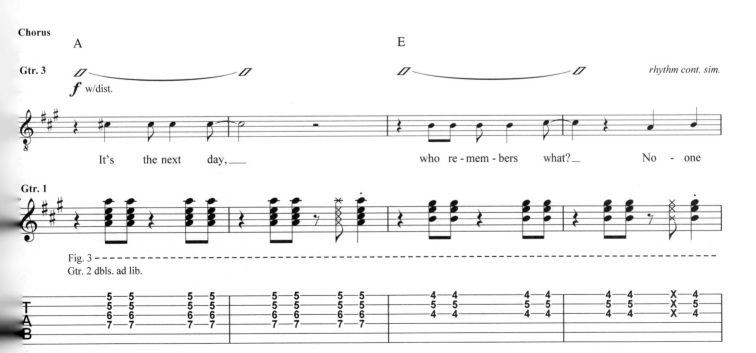

It's the next day, ___ who re - mem - bers what?___ No - one

Gtr. 1

Fig. 3 -
Gtr. 2 dbls. ad lib.

70

Coda

Gtr. 1 plays Fig. 1
Gtr. 2 plays Fig. 2

She won-ders if I re-mem-ber, I was wast-ed an-y-way.

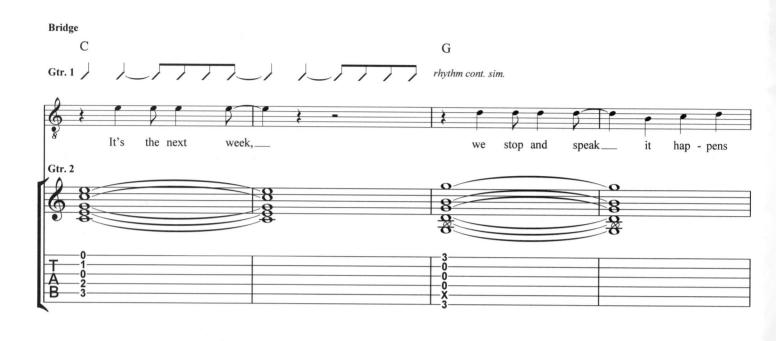

Bridge

It's the next week,___ we stop and speak___ it hap-pens

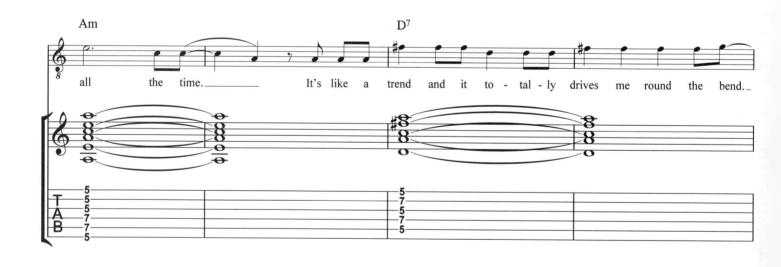

all the time._____ It's like a trend and it to-tal-ly drives me round the bend.__

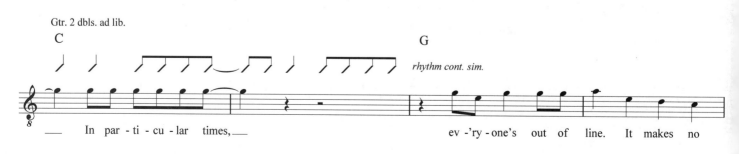

Gtr. 2 dbls. ad lib.

___ In par-ti-cu-lar times,___ ev-'ry-one's out of line. It makes no

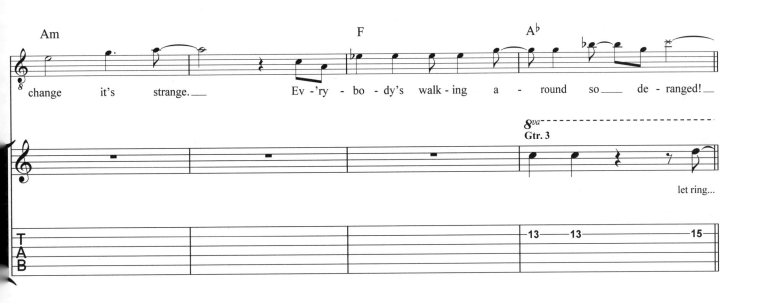

change it's strange.___ Ev-'ry - bo - dy's walk-ing a - round so___ de - ranged!___

Gtr. 3

let ring...

Interlude

Gtr. 1 plays Fig. 1
Gtr. 2 plays Fig. 2

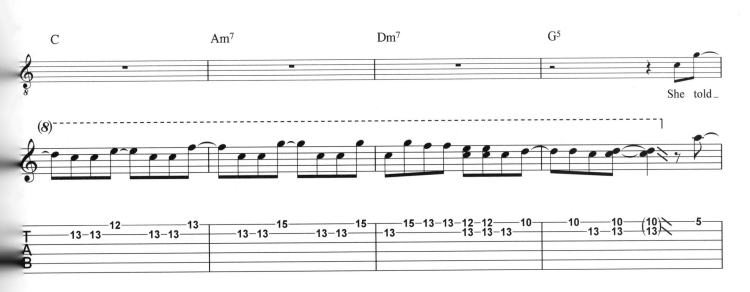

She told___

claudia

Words & Music by
Kyle Falconer & Keiren Webster

78

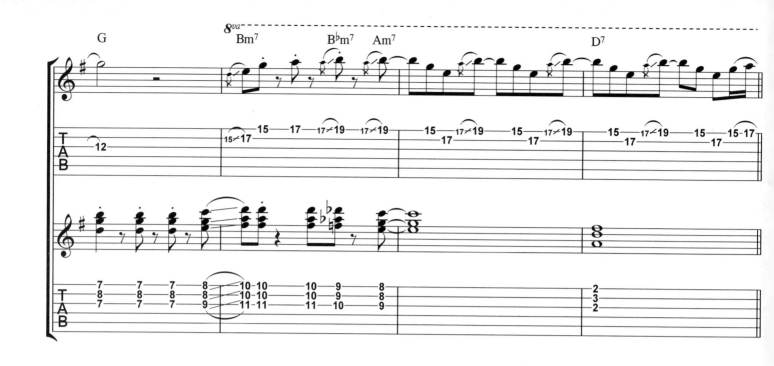

Verse

2. I blame it on your___ up-bring-ing,___ you were made a-round the side of a van.___

Gtr. 1 tacet

Gtr. 4 tacet

You call me the trust - ed one,___ but trust it comes ea-sy, man,_____ ah.

let ring...

streetlights

Words & Music by
Kyle Falconer & Keiren Webster

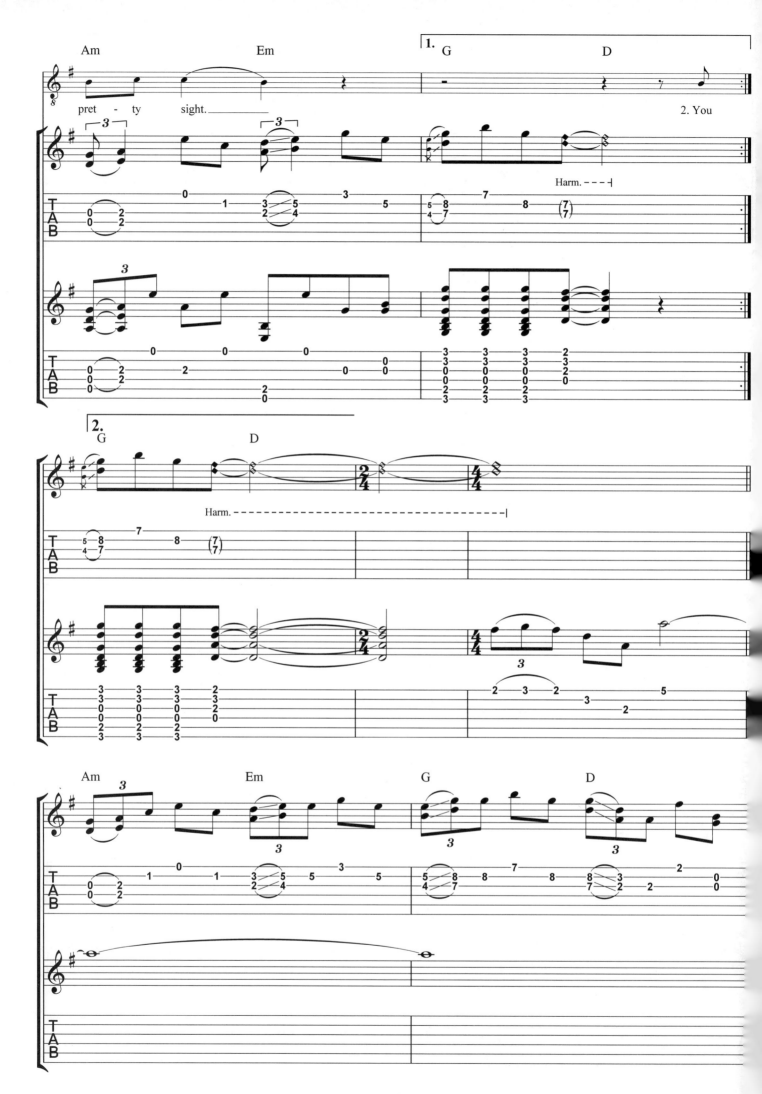

Gtr. 1 plays Fig. 4
Gtr. 2 plays Fig. 5

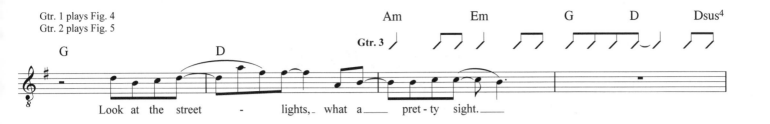

Look at the street - lights,_ what a_____ pret - ty sight.____

Gtrs. 1+2+3

Look at the street - lights,_ what a_____ pret - ty sight._

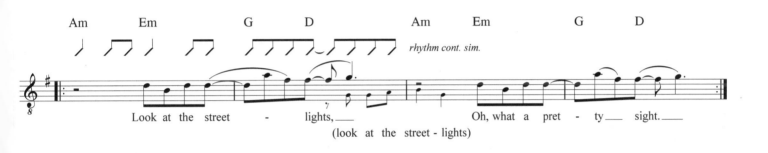

Look at the street - lights,___ Oh, what a pret - ty___ sight.___
(look at the street - lights)

Outro

Gtr. 1 plays Fig. 1

Gtr. 2

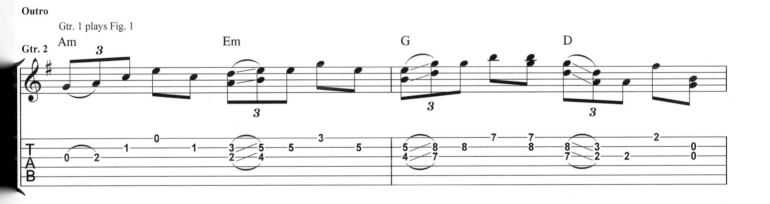

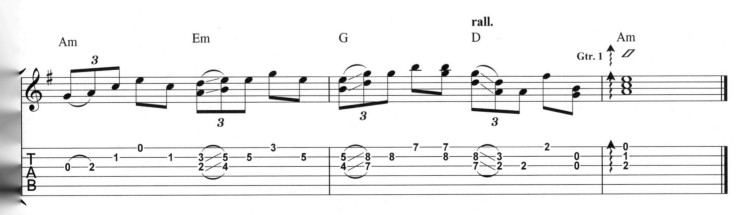

rall.

wasteland

Words & Music by
Kyle Falconer & Keiren Webster

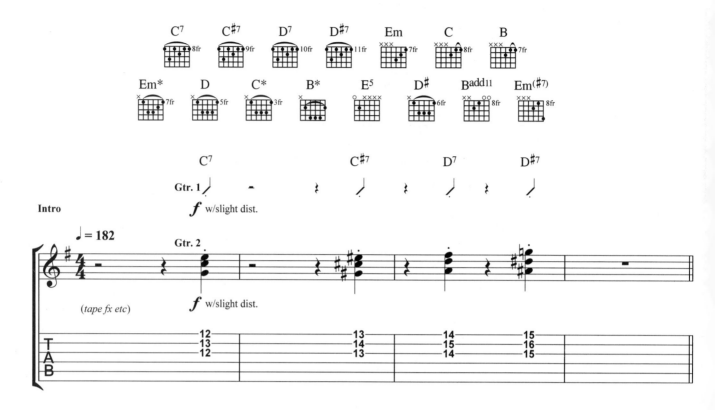

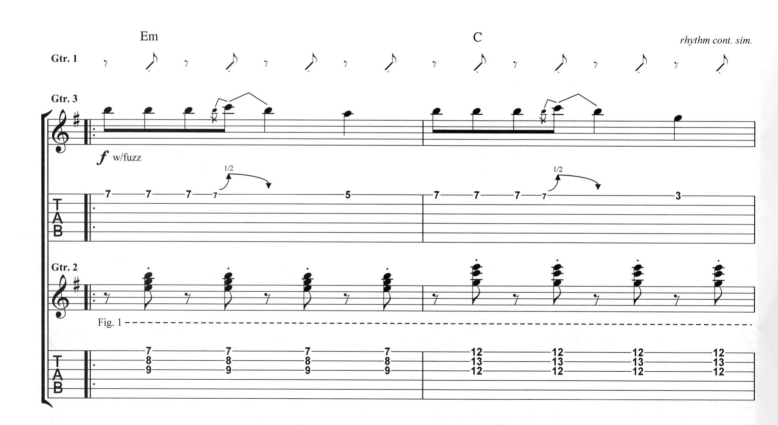

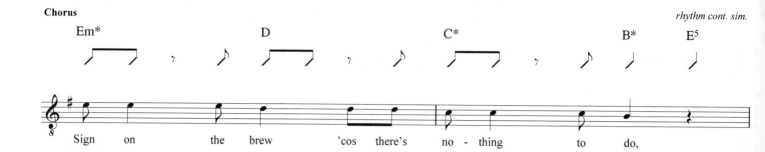

Sign on the brew 'cos there's no - thing to do,

no - thing to do but lis - ten to you. Not list - 'ning to you, my

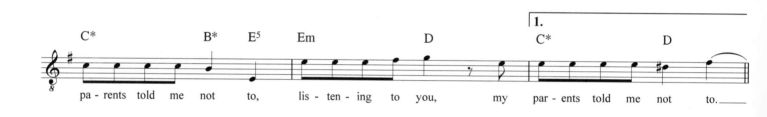

pa - rents told me not to, lis - ten - ing to you, my par - ents told me not to.

Gtr. 2 plays Fig. 1

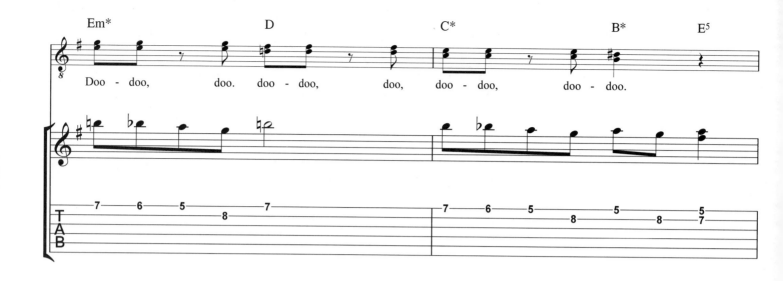

Doo - doo,   doo. doo - doo,   doo,   doo - doo,   doo - doo.

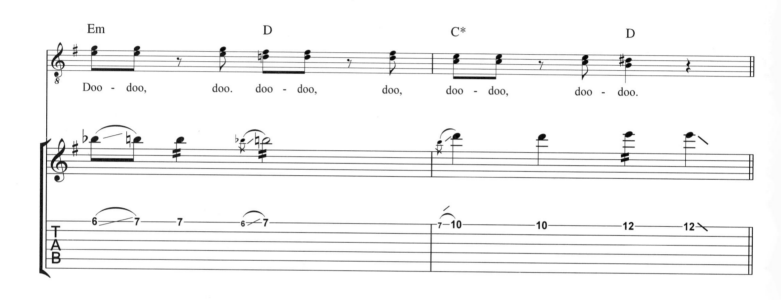

Doo - doo,   doo. doo - doo,   doo,   doo - doo,   doo - doo.

Bridge

Gtrs. 1+2+3

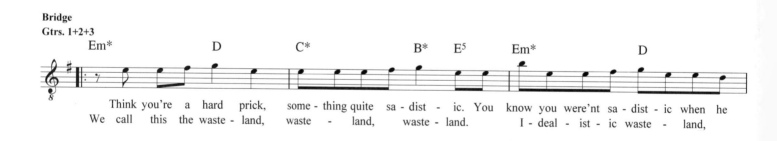

Think you're a hard prick,   some - thing quite sa - dist - ic. You   know you were'nt sa - dist - ic when he
We   call   this the waste - land,   waste - land,   waste - land.   I - deal - ist - ic waste - land,

done you with the brick, Rick.   Your land   is   bor - ing, so   ve - ry,   ve - ry   bor - ing. You
waste - land,   waste - land.   This   is   a   waste - land   a   jour - nal - ist - ic   waste - land.

typical time

Words & Music by
Kyle Falconer & Keiren Webster

GUITAR TABLATURE EXPLAINED

Guitar music can be notated in three different ways: on a musical stave, in tablature, and in rhythm slashes.

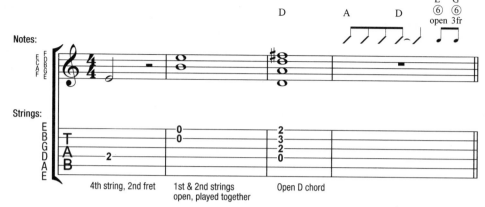

RHYTHM SLASHES: are written above the stave. Strum chords in the rhythm indicated. Round noteheads indicate single notes.

THE MUSICAL STAVE: shows pitches and rhythms and is divided by lines into bars. Pitches are named after the first seven letters of the alphabet.

TABLATURE: graphically represents the guitar fingerboard. Each horizontal line represents a string, and each number represents a fret.

4th string, 2nd fret   1st & 2nd strings open, played together   Open D chord

Definitions for special guitar notation

SEMI-TONE BEND: Strike the note and bend up a semi-tone (½ step).

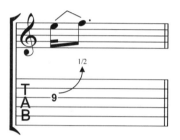

WHOLE-TONE BEND: Strike the note and bend up a whole-tone (full step).

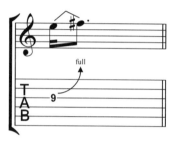

GRACE NOTE BEND: Strike the note and bend as indicated. Play the first note as quickly as possible.

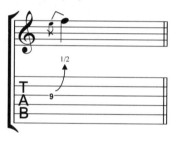

QUARTER-TONE BEND: Strike the note and bend up a ¼ step.

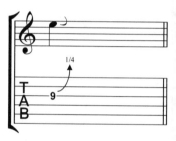

BEND & RELEASE: Strike the note and bend up as indicated, then release back to the original note.

COMPOUND BEND & RELEASE: Strike the note and bend up and down in the rhythm indicated.

PRE-BEND: Bend the note as indicated, then strike it.

PRE-BEND & RELEASE: Bend the note as indicated. Strike it and release the note back to the original pitch.

HAMMER-ON: Strike the first note with one finger, then sound the second note (on the same string) with another finger by fretting it without picking.

PULL-OFF: Place both fingers on the note to be sounded, strike the first note and without picking, pull the finger off to sound the second note.

LEGATO SLIDE (GLISS): Strike the first note and then slide the same fret-hand finger up or down to the second note. The second note is not struck.

MUFFLED STRINGS: A percussive sound is produced by laying the first hand across the string(s) without depressing, and striking them with the pick hand.

NATURAL HARMONIC: Strike the note while the fret-hand lightly touches the string directly over the fret indicated.

PICK SCRAPE: The edge of the pick is rubbed down (or up) the string, producing a scratchy sound.

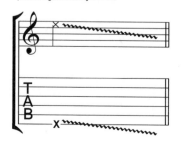

PALM MUTING: The note is partially muted by the pick hand lightly touching the string(s) just before the bridge.

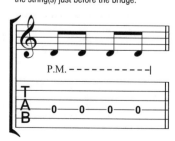

SHIFT SLIDE (GLISS & RESTRIKE): Same as legato slide, except the second note is struck.